The Chr

By **Lisa Young** anc

Illustrations by
Leela Holland

A ***Moving On*** Book

Publisher:
Robert Dawson/Derbyshire Gypsy Liaison Group

2003

Publisher Robert Dawson on behalf of
Derbyshire Gypsy Liaison Group
188 Alfreton Road, Blackwell
Alfreton, Derbys DE55 5JH

ISBN 1-903418-35-6

Printed by 4 Sheets Design and Print Ltd.,
197 Mansfield Road, Nottingham NG1 3FS

My sister Rosie is having her baby christened.

She is a lovely little girl and is to be named Rosie after my sister

I am going
to be
Godmother

My family have to travel to London in time for the christening

We took our trailer and pulled onto a site near to my sister

Rosie is going to wear a frilly white christening gown

And she is
having a cake
with her name
on

I felt very grown up being asked to be Godmother

There were lots of people in the church

I got to hold Rosie in the church

The Minister took her off me and put water on Rosie's head and said her names

He then gave Rosie back to her mam and dad

After the service in the church we all had a party

Rosie got lots of presents and we all had a good time.

Then it was time to travel back home ready for school

I had a nice time in London. I can't wait until my next visit to see Rosie

The Christening

MOVING ON series

Acknowledgement

From a proposal by Lancashire Traveller Education Consortium who would like to thank all colleagues who have given help and advice in the production of this book, with a special thanks to all those families who have welcomed us into their homes and shared their knowledge with us.

Thanks too to Derby and Derbyshire TES for finding Leela and to her parents and grandparents for inspiring and encouraging Leela to develop her skills

Derbyshire Gypsy Liaison Group acknowledges with gratitude, funding assistance given by the Esmee Fairbairn Foundation and by the Tudor Trust without whom these books would not have been possible.

The Moving On Series

100+ Culture-specific books for Traveller children

Pre-school/Toddler
4 planned

Key Stage 1
Houses and Homes

Key Stage 1 and 2
When Little Monsters Come to Call
Finches
Dogs
Holiday bus

Key Stage 2
How Rabbits Arrived in England
The Christening
Wagons
Travel
Boxing
Old Crafts
The Rainbow Has No End
3 Mullo stories

Key Stage 3
Hell and Damp Nation